by Jules Feiffer

INTRODUCTION by KENNETH TYNAN

Collins, St. James's Place, London

FIRST IMPRESSION   OCTOBER 1959
SECOND IMPRESSION   NOVEMBER 1959

LIBRARY OF CONGRESS CATALOGUE CARD NO. 58-9926
The cartoons in this book appeared in *The Village Voice*, New York, and *The Observer*, London
PRINTED IN GREAT BRITAIN
COLLINS CLEAR-TYPE PRESS: LONDON AND GLASGOW

Introduction
by Kenneth Tynan

The American comic strip has always struck me as one of the more over-rated aspects of transatlantic culture, in which it plays a part not unlike that of the detective story in Britain. Everyone reads the strips; and when, as occasionally happens, an artist manages to inject into them some reference or allusion that defines him as a man who left school at an age later than fifteen, the intelligentsia is prone to hail him a genius. John Steinbeck, for example, once said that Al Capp, the creator of " L'il Abner," was perhaps the greatest satirist since the eighteenth century, and there are plenty of people in Manhattan who will assert that nothing in American journalism is as brilliant as Walt Kelly's " Pogo " strip in *The New York Post*. The truth is that, although Messrs. Capp and Kelly frequently use their backwoods characters for purposes of social or political comment—some of it wickedly pungent—they are basically working with a traditional formula. They have to tell a story, and they have to tell it on a mass-circulation scale, which necessarily means that there are limits to the amount of intellectual contraband they can smuggle into print.

Enfin Feiffer *vint*. And with him came change. When Jules Feiffer's cartoons started to appear in *The Village Voice*, a raffish radical weekly that speaks for Greenwich Village, that island within an island, it was immediately clear that a minor revolution was taking place in the art of drawing pictures for newspapers. For one thing, Feiffer had no stories to tell. His main concern was to explore character. In a series of a dozen or so pictures, he would show the shifts of mood that flickered across the faces of men and women as they tried, often vainly, to explain themselves to the world, to their husbands and wives, to their mistresses and lovers, to their employers, to their rulers, or simply to the unseen adversaries at the other end of the telephone wires. Many of Feiffer's characters are monologuists. They apologise and over-apologise; they explain and over-explain; and quite often we begin by scoffing at them and end up pitying them. They come, for the most part, from a group that is restricted but wonderfully representative—the educated East Coasters, who include the advertising men of Madison Avenue, the real Bohemians of Greenwich Village as well as the pseudoes, the college boys venturing for the first time into the big world of income tax, and the Zen beatniks hoping to opt out of it.

They are all full of words. It may sound an odd tribute to pay a cartoonist, but I doubt whether Feiffer has a more valuable attribute, as a graphic artist, than his ear. He *listens*, both attentively and retentively; so much so that I would hate to occupy a booth in a Village restaurant with Feiffer on the other side of the partition. "Fougasse," many years ago, introduced to *Punch* the idea that Feiffer has since developed and perfected, probably without knowing where it came from—the idea of building a page of illustrated comedy on the small changes of expression that cross the faces of people to whom nothing in particular is happening except talk and thought. Apart from having the eye of a draughtsman, Feiffer has the ear of a novelist or playwright. It would be no exaggeration to say that his dialogue is as acute as any that is being written in America to-day.

It is, above all, dialogue aimed at sophisticated minds, usually with the purpose of shaking them out of sophistication into real awareness. Those who become slaves to non-conformity are as much Feiffer's targets as those who are ruled by conformity; he prods not only organisation men but those whose Bible is " The Organisation Man." Yet always he presses his points obliquely, by letting his characters convict themselves out of their own mouths. . By an accident of history, and perhaps against his will, he has become part of a movement; his attitudes and his idiom belong to the same upsurge of " hip " protest that created such iconoclastic comedians as Mort Sahl and Lenny Bruce. It is a tribute to something—conceivably to America—that Feiffer's drawings are now on view in fifty newspapers outside New York. Any of them can reject what he offers, but none may tamper with it. His arrangement with *The Observer* is founded on the same principle; the paper buys what it wants of him, but his work, once bought, is inviolable.

You cannot live for long in New York without meeting Feiffer characters—people sodden with the clichés of the advertising game, people talking endlessly and deafly, people trying to justify themselves through jargons that fail to communicate with anyone else, people governed by verbal concepts that serve as smoke-screens between them and reality, heavy suave people, light insecure people, all of them betraying themselves in multitudinous ways, by turns of phrase, twinges of visage and shrugs of shoulders. They exist, as by now you should guess, in England too. Feiffer is their lively and not unloving chronicler—the watcher who bears sardonic witness to the fact that most human beings do not trust themselves enough to be themselves. As I closed his book, I felt that he regarded the human race with condign affection, but that he doubted whether it needed to race so fast to be human.

Feiffer is young—thirty years old—and his first cartoon appeared in *The Village Voice* less than three years ago. He calls this collection " Sick, Sick, Sick." A misnomer: I would have dubbed it " Sane, Sane, Sane." And in case I forgot to mention it, he is also profoundly funny.

I was
feeling
lonely and
unnoticed.

But then
I got
a
hoop.

And I spun
my hoop like
this

And soon
all the girls
were noticing
me.

And I
spun my
hoop like
this.

And soon all the
boys were notic-
ing me.

So I spun my
hoop like this.

And then a
crowd of men
noticed
me.

And they all
had a funny
kind of grin.

Then my
mother came
out and
beat me
up.

TODAY'S BOOK IS A RATHER BULKY BUT PROMISING FIRST ATTEMPT BY AUTHOR OR AUTHORS UNKNOWN.

IT'S CALLED "THE BIBLE."

IT IS WRITTEN IN A NARRATIVE RATHER THAN INTROSPECTIVE STYLE WHICH MAY PERHAPS MAKE FOR QUICKER READING BUT LEAVES SOMETHING TO BE DESIRED ON THE LEVEL OF CHARACTER MOTIVATION.

IT PURPORTS TO BE A THEOLOGICAL AND HISTORICAL DOCUMENT AND WHILE THIS REVIEWER DOES NOT QUESTION ITS SINCERITY, HE CAN ONLY REGRET THE PUBLISHER'S FAILURE TO INCLUDE A BIBLIOGRAPHY.

BUT THESE ARE MINOR CRITICISMS. ONE CAN NOT DENY THE POWER AND SWEEPING RANGE OF THE SUBJECT MATTER - (ONE MIGHT EVEN CALL IT EPIC) -

- THE SUBTLE ALLEGORICAL NUANCES TOUCHED, AT TIMES, WITH WHAT SEEMS TO BE AN ALMOST METAPHYSICAL INSIGHT! IT WILL UNDOUBTEDLY CAUSE CONTROVERSY IN THE LITERARY FIELD.

BUT THE AUTHORS, WHILE WRITING IN A QUASI-JOURNALISTIC FORM SHOW OCCASIONAL FLOURISHES OF STYLISTIC DARING WHICH MAKES ONE IMPATIENT TO VIEW THEIR LATER EFFORTS.

I SHALL AWAIT THEIR SECOND BOOK WITH GREAT INTEREST.

GO AHEAD! **EAT** ME! PLAY INTO **THEIR** HANDS.

PLEASE. MUST WE CONTINUALLY BICKER? CAN'T WE JUST ACCEPT OUR GIVEN ROLES?

OF COURSE. **YOU'D** SAY THAT. REFUSAL TO CHANGE IS A CHARACTERISTIC OF YOUR CLASS.

LOOK. I'M NOT AGAINST INTELLIGENT CHANGE. BUT THIS QUESTION HAS BEEN LOOKED INTO BEFORE. CATS HAVE **ALWAYS** KILLED MICE. IT'S A TRADITION.

AN OUTMODED RITUAL UNFIT FOR TODAY'S HUMANISTIC VALUES. DON'T YOU SEE WHO PROFITS MOST FROM THE UNNATURAL EMNITY BETWEEN OUR PEOPLES?

YOUR KIND ALWAYS HAS TO LOOK FOR VILLAINS. IT BORES ME.

HOW INCREDIBLY NAIVE! WHOSE ENDS DO YOU **REALLY** SERVE? WHO GAINS BY DIVERTING BOTH OF US INTO A **USELESS** STRUGGLE THAT CAN'T **EVER** END?

:SIGH: I SUPPOSE YOU'LL TELL ME WHETHER I WANT TO HEAR OR NOT.

IT'S **MAN!** YOU SILLY INNOCENT! **MAN!**

OH, COME NOW. MAN PETS ME. MAN GIVES ME FOOD.

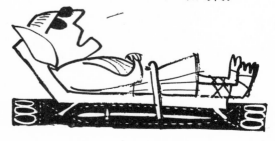

ALL RIGHT, BUT ITS WHAT I WANT TO DO.

5.

INSTEAD I HAVE TO GO ON **PAINTING** ALL DAY LONG.

6.

7.

THE WORLD SHOULD MAKE A PLACE FOR SHOE SALESMEN.

8.

VERY GOOD. VERY GOOD.
FOR A MOMENT THERE
I ALMOST FELT AROUSED.
I GUESS ITS BECAUSE
THEY'RE SO CURRENT.

DO YOU THINK
WE'VE TURNED
APATHETIC ?

APATHY IS SUCH A
BAD WORD. I'D HATE
TO THINK ITS
APATHY WE SUFFER
FROM.

LETS JUST
CALL IT
FAITH.

A
DANCE
TO
SPRING.

1.

2.

3.

4.

6.

7.

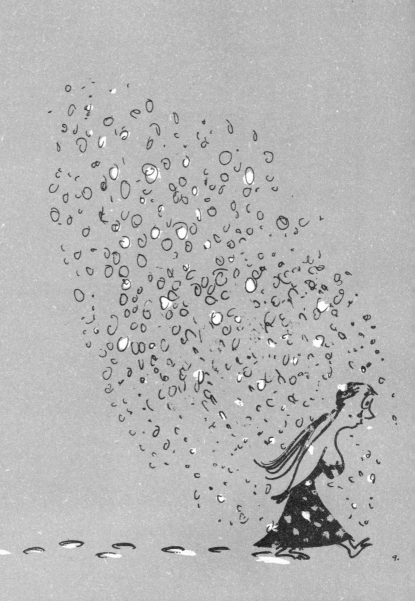

9.

I KEEP RUNNING BUT I DON'T GET ANYWHERE.

HI THERE HOWARD.

MURRAY'S A GOOD EGG. I SHOULD BE **GLAD** TO SEE HIM GET AHEAD. I WON'T BE BITTER.

HELLO AND GOODBYE — HOWARD.

LUCILLE HAS **LOOKS**.
NO WONDER SHE GETS AHEAD.
I BET SHE USES HER **BODY**.
BUT I WON'T BE BITTER.

*WATCH MY SPEED,
HOWARD.*

IRWIN IS FIVE YEARS YOUNGER THAN ME AND A NO GOOD PUNK!

I KNOW
I'D DO
BETTER
IF NOT
FOR THESE
STOMACH
ACHES.

SO I WAS STANDING ON
THE CORNER WAITING FOR
SOMEBODY TO CROSS ME
BECAUSE I'M NOT ALLOWED
TO CROSS BY MYSELF.

AND THIS LADY COMES
BY AND SHE SAYS -
"HERE IS A BUBBLE GUM
SAMPLE. DO YOU CHEW
THIS BRAND?"

AND I SAYS - "I DON'T
LIKE BUBBLE GUM". SO
THIS LADY TAKES OUT A
PAD AND SHE STARTS
WRITING AND THEN SHE
SAYS - "WHY
DON'T YOU
LIKE IT?
IS IT THE
DESIGN OF
THE WRAPPER?"

AND I SAYS -
"NO ITS 'CAUSE
I CAN'T BLOW
BUBBLES."

SO SHE WRITES THAT DOWN ON
HER PAD AND THEN SHE SAYS -
"HOW WOULD YOU LIKE A
BUBBLE GUM WHICH WAS
GUARANTEED TO BLOW
BUBBLES?"

AND I SAYS - "I DON'T KNOW -
I CAN'T WHISTLE THROUGH
MY FINGERS EITHER"

"AND I CAN'T CROSS
THE STREET BY
MYSELF AND MY
TEACHERS SAY
I DON'T
TRY -"

"AND WHEN WE PLAY GAMES I'M ALWAYS 'IT' AND I'M NEVER ALLOWED TO WATCH WHAT **I** WANT AND MY FATHER KEEPS CALLING ME BY MY OLDER SISTER'S NAME—"

AND ALL OF A SUDDEN I'M CRYING LIKE MAD AND THIS LADY IS WRITING AWAY ON HER PAD AND SHE'S CRYING TOO—

AND I SAY—"SO YOU SEE— IT HAS **NOTHING** TO DO WITH YOUR BUBBLE GUM! **IT'S ME! IT'S ALL ME!**

AND I'M SHOUTING AND CRYING AND THE LADY IS WRITING AWAY AND A CROWD COMES ALONG.

AND SOME BIG GUY SAYS— "IS THIS LADY BOTHERING YOU, GIRLIE?" AND THE CROWD TURNS UGLY.

SO THE LADY GETS VERY NERVOUS AND SHE STARTS HANDING OUT BUBBLE GUM TO EVERYBODY AND SHE DROPS HER PAD IN THE STREET—

AND SHE'S ASKING EVERYBODY—"WHY DON'T YOU LIKE IT? IS IT THE DESIGN OF THE WRAPPER?" AND NOBODY KNOWS WHAT SHE'S TALKING ABOUT.

SO THEN I WENT HOME.

THE MEETING OF THE "I'M JUST DOING MY JOB CLUB" WILL COME TO ORDER. WE WILL BEGIN WITH A REPORT FROM MEMBER, ROCKWELL J.

I BEGAN AS A MONITOR IN GRAMMAR SCHOOL. WHEN I WAS CALLED DOWN FOR REPORTING MY CLASS MATES, I SIMPLY ANSWERED - "DON'T BLAME ME. I WAS **TOLD** TO DO IT.

PROMISING

VERY PROMISING.

LATER ON I WAS IN THE MILITARY SERVICE. IT WAS MY JOB TO CLASSIFY PERSONNEL. I DIDN'T **LIKE** TO SEND MEN TO WAR. BUT THOSE WERE MY **ORDERS**. I HAD NO CHOICE.

AFTER SERVICE I HAD TROUBLE FINDING MY NICHE. FOR AWHILE I WAS REALTY AGENT FOR A SLUM. THE TENANTS DIDN'T UNDERSTAND. I WAS JUST DOING WHAT I WAS HIRED TO DO.

REASONABLE!

QUITE REASONABLE!

RESPONSIBLE!

HIGHLY RESPONSIBLE!

XT I WENT TO WORK AS A WITNESS. APPEARED BEFORE DOZENS OF. NGRESSIONAL COMMITTEES. I DIDN'T KE THE WORK. BUT I **HAD** TO DO AT I WAS BEING PAID FOR.

AND NOW I'VE REACHED THE **PINNACLE!** I'VE GONE TO WORK IN A STATE PRISON. I DON'T NECESSARILY BELIEVE IN CAPITAL PUNISHMENT BUT **SOMEONE** HAS TO PULL THE SWITCH.

OF COURSE **SOME** PEOPLE DON'T UNDERSTAND. THEY ASSOCIATE **ME** WITH THE WAY I MAKE A LIVING.

NEXT WE HEAR FROM MEMBER ARNOLD K. HE WILL SPEAK ON INTERCONTINENTAL BALLISTIC MISSILES.

I **USED** TO BE A REBEL IN MY YOUTH.

1.

THIS CAUSE... **THAT** CAUSE... (CHUCKLE) I BACKED 'EM **ALL**.

2.

BUT I LEARNED.

3.

REBELLION IS SIMPLY A **DEVICE** USED BY THE IMMATURE TO **HIDE** FROM HIS OWN PROBLEMS.

4.

SO I LOST INTEREST IN POLITICS.

5.

NOW WHEN I FEEL AROUSED
BY A **CIVIL RIGHTS** CASE
OR A **PASSPORT** HEARING....

6.

I **REALIZE** IT'S
JUST A DEVICE.

7.

I GO TO MY ANALYST
AND WE WORK IT OUT.

8.

YOU HAVE NO IDEA HOW
MUCH **BETTER** I FEEL
THESE DAYS.

9.

SOME PEOPLE SEE **EVERYTHING** IN TERMS OF BLACK AND WHITE.

BUT NOT ME. **I** LOOK FOR THE **MIDDLE TONES.**

1.

2.

LIKE MOST GIRLS IF THEIR BLIND DATE LEAVES THEM IN A RESTAURANT TO MAKE A PHONE CALL AND HE DOESN'T COME BACK... THEY'D SEE THAT IN TERMS OF BLACK AND WHITE.

BUT NOT ME. **I** LOOK FOR **MOTIVATION.**

3.

4.

LIKE.... OR ERRATIC INTERPERSONAL
COMPULSIVE   ADJUSTMENTS
SOCIAL
BEHAVIOR   OR
PATTERNS.   HOSTILE
                 GROUP
                 ATTITUDES.

THERE MUST BE SOME
BASIC DRIVE THAT MAKES
           HIM FLEE
           FROM A
           BLIND
           DATE.

5.

6.

SO WHY GET UPSET? IT HAS
NOTHING TO DO WITH **ME**
        PERSONALLY.

I HOPE HE WORKS IT OUT
SOON. I'M GETTING TIRED
OF WAITING.

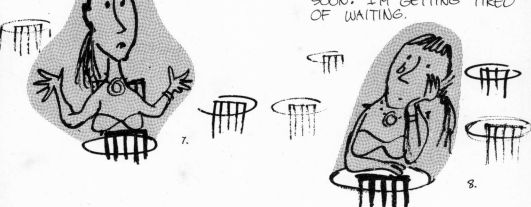

7.

8.

COME OVER HERE
AND KISS YOUR
AUNT PEGGY
GOODBYE!

I SWEAR, PEGGY— HIM AND
HIS LITTLE BROTHER—
IT'S LIKE **DAY AND NIGHT**.

SEE HOW NICE YOUR
LITTLE BROTHER HUGS
YOUR AUNT PEGGY?

ONE IS GOOD AS GOLD.
THE OTHER IS NOTHING BUT
TROUBLE. **ARE YOU
COMING OVER HERE?**

ISN'T THAT A GEM? LOOK HOW
THE LITTLE ONE LAUGHS
EVERYTIME I YELL AT HIS
BIG BROTHER. HE'S **ALWAYS**
HAPPY.

SEE HOW YOUR LITTLE
BROTHER IS LAUGHING
AT YOU?

YOU'RE NOT HERE IN
E SECOND FLAT
SMACK YOU AND **THEN**
TCH HIM LAUGH.

my leg
hurts

(CHUCKLE) HIS LEG
ALWAYS HURTS WHEN
I YELL AT HIM.

I SWEAR, PEGGY,
SOMETIMES KIDS
ARE BEYOND ME.

I'M **ALWAYS** HAVING A GOOD TIME.

1.

MOST PEOPLE **HATE** THEIR JOBS. I'VE BEEN HERE **FIFTEEN** YEARS.

2.

LOVED **EVERY** MINUTE OF IT.

3.

SEEN BOSSES COME - SEEN BOSSES GO. I **JOKED** WITH 'EM ALL.

4.

THAT'S BECAUSE I KNOW HOW TO GET ALONG.

5.

I KID THE
OFFICE STAFF.
TELL 'EM GAGS
ON THE BOSS..

6.

THEY EAT
IT UP.

7.

BUT THEN I
COOPERATE
WITH THE
BOSS **TOO.**

8.

... LIKE I TELL HIM WHO
COMES IN LATE AND
WHO SPENDS TIME
IN THE WASHROOM...

9.

THEY CALL
ME MR.
SUNSHINE.

10.

1. THE ITEM ON THE AGENDA, GENTLEMEN, IS THE **FALLOUT** BIT. OUR CLIENT ISN'T HAPPY WITH OUR CAMPAIGN.

2. THE PUBLIC IS **NEGATIVE** FALLOUT CONSCIOUS. WE MUST MAKE THEM **POSITIVE** FALLOUT CONSCIOUS.

3. I HAVE HERE THE OUTLINE OF A *"FALLOUT IS GOOD FOR YOU"* SATURATION CAMPAIGN.

4. IT INCLUDES SUCH ITEMS AS *"I LIKE FALLOUT"* BUTTONS, DECALS INSCRIBED WITH *"YOUR GOVERNMENT KNOWS BEST"* — A TV SPEC CALLED *"I FELL FOR FALLOUT"*

AND AS A CAPPER - A "MR. AND MRS. MUTATION" CONTEST- DESIGNED TO CHANGE THE CONCEPT OF **BEAUTY** IN THE AMERICAN MIND.

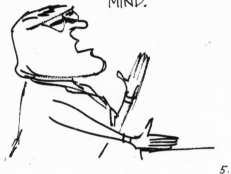

5.

BUT WHAT ABOUT THE **SCIENTISTS**, CHIEF?

6.

NO PROBLEM. WE'LL SAY THEY'RE "**ORGANIZED**" AND HAVE THEM ALL SUBPOENAED.

7.

IT'S ONE OF OUR MOST SUCCESSFUL SALES DEVICES.

8.

WELCOME BACK FOR YOUR 13th CONSECUTIVE WEEK, EVELYN.

THANK YOU, RED.

1.

EVELYN, WILL YOU GO INTO THE AUTO-SUGGESTION BOOTH AND TAKE YOUR REGULAR PLACE ON THE PSYCHO-PROMPTER COUCH?

THANK YOU, RED.

2.

NOW, EVELYN, LAST WEEK YOU WENT UP TO $40,000 BY PROPERLY CITING YOUR RIVALRY WITH YOUR SIBLING AS A COMPULSIVE SADO-MASOCHISTIC BEHAVIOR PATTERN WHICH DEVELOPED OUT OF AN EARLY POST-NATAL FEEDING PROBLEM.

YES, RED.

3.

BUT— LATER, WHEN ASKED ABOUT PRE-ADOLESCENT OEDIPAL PHANTASY REPRESSIONS, YOU **RATIONALIZED** TWICE AND **MENTAL BLOCKED** THREE TIMES.

4.

NOW AT **$300** PER RATIONALIZATION AND **$500** PER MENTAL BLOCK YOU **LOST** $2,100 OFF YOUR $40,000 LEAVING YOU WITH A TOTAL OF $37,900!

YES, RED

5.

NOW, **ANY** COMBINATION OF **TWO** MORE MENTAL BLOCKS AND **EITHER ONE** RATIONALIZATION OR **THREE** DEFENSIVE PROJECTIONS WILL PUT YOU **OUT OF THE GAME.** ARE YOU WILLING TO GO AHEAD?

YES, RED.

6.

I MIGHT SAY HERE THAT
ALL OF EVELYN'S
QUESTIONS AND ANSWERS
HAVE BEEN CHECKED FOR
ACCURACY WITH HER
ANALYST. ,

7.

NOW EVELYN, FOR $80,000
EXPLAIN THE FAILURE OF
YOUR THREE MARRIAGES.

WELL
I —

8.

WE'LL GET BACK TO
EVELYN IN **ONE**
MINUTE. **FIRST** A
WORD ABOUT OUR
PRODUCT. ,

9.

NOW LET
ME MAKE
MYSELF
CLEAR.

1.

NOW WE HAVE A LAW AND WE
ARE A COUNTRY GOVERNED BY
LAW. I WANT YOU TO KNOW
I FEEL **STRONGLY** ABOUT
THAT.

2.

NOW THERE ARE LAWS WE LIKE
AND LAWS WE DON'T LIKE. BUT—
AND I WANT TO MAKE THIS
CLEAR— WE MUST **OBEY** OUR
LAWS OR ELSE
WE COULD AID
COMMUNISM.

3.

NOW HERE IS THE
LAW OF THE LAND.
AND THAT IS THAT
AND WE MUST
ENFORCE IT.

4.

NOW THE REST OF THE
WORLD IS WATCHING—
LET ME MAKE THAT
CLEAR—AND WHETHER
WE LIKE IT OR NOT—
LOTS OF THEM
ARE **COLORED**.

5.

BUT THAT'S **NATURE'S**
LAW AND WE MUST
LIVE WITH IT.
I CAN'T STRESS
THAT TOO FIRMLY.

6.

NOW LET'S PULL
TOGETHER
VOLUNTARILY
AND THAT WILL
SOLVE IT ALL
AND WHETHER
WE LIKE IT OR
NOT-FORGE
AHEAD.

7.

AND THE REST
OF THE WORLD
WILL RESPECT US
FOR OUR MORAL
STAND.

8.

WE MUST BE MAKING OUT LIKE ITS WORLD WAR II

LIKE IN THE MOVIES.

I MUST BE THE GOOD GUY— THE AMERICAN—

I MUST BE THE OTHER GOOD GUY— THE NAZI! I HAVE THE BEST UNIFORM!

I MUST BE WISHY WASHY BUT SENSITIVE.

I MUST BE MEAN AND BRUTAL— BUT THERE ARE REASONS.

I MUST HAVE TO CHASE YOU. BUT I REALLY WANT TO BE HOME RAKING UP THE OLD LAWN

I MUST HAVE TO CHASE YOU TOO. BUT ITS ONLY BECAUSE I'M MADE TO.

I MUST HAVE TO SHOOT AT YOU. BUT I REALLY WANT TO BE HOME TINKERING WITH MY OLD FORD.

I MUST HAVE TO SHOOT AT YOU TOO. BUT I'M JUST DOING MY JOB.

WE WANT YOU TO FEEL HAPPY ON THE JOB, HOWARD—AND A MAN WHO **STRIDES** IN HERE AND **DEMANDS** MORE MONEY— WELL, THAT'S NOT A HAPPY MAN, HOWARD.

5.

NOW, PERHAPS YOU'D BE HAPPIER SOMEWHERE ELSE.

6.

BUT THAT'S **YOUR** DECISION TO MAKE, FELLA. TAKE **ALL** THE TIME YOU LIKE.

7.

I'LL JUST GO ON SIGNING THESE PAPERS.

8.

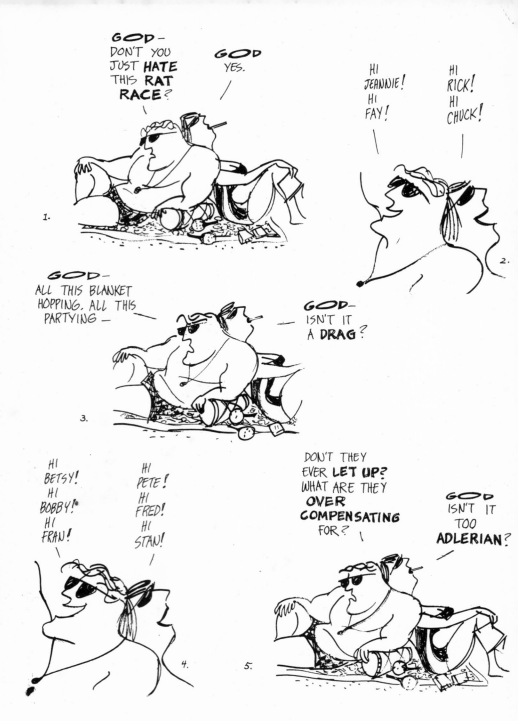

ELEVEN
YEARS
OLD AND
I'M
NEVER
PICKED
FOR THE
TEAM.

1.

LOOK AT
THOSE
OTHERS.
THEY
ALWAYS
PLAY.

2.

BATTING THE
BALL...
CATCHING IT.

3.

RUNNING...
LAUGHING...

4.

5.

THERE'S
SOMETHING
BASICALLY
WRONG
THERE.

6.

SOMETHING
BAD.
SOMETHING
UNHEALTHY.

7.

THE WAY THEY
GATHER
TOGETHER.
THE WAY THEY
CHOOSE
UP SIDES.

8.

IT'S VERY
LUCKY THEY
WON'T LET
ME PLAY.

9.

OTHERWISE
I MIGHT
NOT HAVE
NOTICED.

MAN, THAT'S
WHAT A
REBEL IS.

1.

I MEAN HE DON'T
TALK UP TO NO
JUDGE. HE DON'T
SAY IT'S A **BAD
RAP.**

2.

'CAUSE HE **KNOWS** HE'S
GUILTY. LIKE TO HIM
JUST **LIVING** IS A
CRIME.

3.

SO HE **CUTS OUT**-
YOU KNOW, MAN –
HE **WITHDRAWS**.

4.

AND HE GOES WITH HIS **OWN** AND HE SAYS, "**SQUARES** I DO NOT **KNOW** YOU." THAT'S **REBELLION** MAN.

AND HE LEARNS A **NEW** TONGUE — LIKE A **DIFFERENT LANGUAGE** — AND WHEN THE SQUARES COME AROUND, HE SAYS "**WHAT** ARE THEY SAYING?" THAT'S **REBELLION** MAN.

5.

6.

AND SOON HE'S **SO** WITHDRAWN HE ONLY HEARS **HIMSELF**. SO HE WRITES IT IN A BOOK.

AND THE SQUARES SAY, "**HEY** — HERE'S THE **LATEST!**"

7.

8.

SO THEY **BUY** HIS WITHDRAWAL AND EVERYONE MAKES A **MINT**.

THAT'S REBELLION, MAN.

9.

10.

1.

2.

3.

4.

5.

THAT WAS ON LAST YEAR'S BOOK LIST. WHAT'S THE **NEW** PASSWORD?

6.

IN GROUP? OUTGROUP? CONFORMIST?

7.

LATENT?
MATERIALISTIC?
MATRIARCHAL?
HOW ABOUT ORWELLIAN—?
THAT'S ALWAYS SAFE.

8.

HE'S NOT AWARE!

9.

NOW THEN, WHAT'S THE PASSWORD?

MOTIVATIONAL RESEARCH

10.

GOOD— WITHOUT THE LATEST PASSWORD WE'D NEVER KNOW WHAT'S WRONG WITH US.

11.

THE **FIRST** ONE
WE BUILT WAS
RELATIVELY
THIS SMALL.

BUT IT
HAD **THIS**
MUCH
FALLOUT—

BUT IN **THOSE**
DAYS FALLOUT
WAS NOT YET
A FAD. SO WE
IGNORED IT.

THE NEXT ONE
WE BUILT WAS
THIS BIG.

BUT IT HAD
THIS MUCH
FALLOUT.

OF COURSE **NONE** OF
US FELT GOOD ABOUT IT.
MY WIFE AND I **DOUBLED**
OUR DONATION TO OUR
REGULAR CHARITIES.

THE **NEXT** ONE WE BUILT WAS **YEA** BIG.

BUT WE HAD REDUCED THE FALLOUT TO **THIS** MUCH.

AND **NOW** AT **LAST** WE HAVE BUILT ONE **SO** BIG IT WILL BLOW UP **EVERY-THING**!

AND ITS 100% **CLEAN**!

WE FEEL OUR PROGRESS HAS BEEN AMAZING.

1.

2.

3.

4.

5.

6.

PROBABLY WON'T LAST THE NIGHT—PROBABLY CRUMBLE AND FALL—WHAT'D **THEY** EVER INVENT THAT WAS ANY GOOD?

7.

8.

BLAST IT OUT OF THE SKY I SAY!

9.

WHAT'S THE USE—? WHAT'S THE SENSE IN GOING ON—?

crack

10.

WE HAVE COMMITTED THE **WORST** OF ALL POSSIBLE SINS—

11.

WE WERE SECOND.

12.

CAN'T YOU **SEE**
BERNARD?
IT'S **NO GOOD.**

1.

YOU'RE A **DOLL** AND
I'M IN**SANE** ABOUT
YOU - BUT IT **REALLY**
WOULDN'T JELL,
BERNARD.

WE'RE **DIFFERENT!**
I'M JUST **MANIC**
FOR PARTIES – FOR
FUN PEOPLE–FOR
HAVING A **BALL.**

2.

3.

AND **YOU**
DIG
TELEVISION.

I WANT TO DANCE AND
FEEL **FREE** – TO GO
BACK TO MAJORCA AND
GAMBLE AND MAKE
LOVE

4.

5.

PUT ON YOUR SHOES – I'LL WALK YOU TO THE SUBWAY.

YOU NEEDN'T BOTHER. I'VE NEVER MET ANYONE SO CRUDE IN MY LIFE.

YEH, CRUDE – NOW PUT ON YOUR SHOES – I'LL WALK YOU TO THE SUBWAY.

YOU WANT EVERYTHING YOUR **OWN** WAY! **YOU'RE SPOILED!**

YEH, SPOILED – NOW PUT ON YOUR SHOES – I'LL WALK YOU TO THE SUBWAY

I DON'T LIKE BEING **PUSHED** INTO THINGS. I NEED A **LITTLE** TIME YOU KNOW!

YEH, TIME – NOW PUT ON YOUR SHOES – I'LL WALK YOU TO THE SUBWAY.

I MEAN – WE'VE HARDLY EVEN **TALKED**.

YEH, TALK – NOW PUT ON YOUR SHOES – I'LL WALK YOU TO THE SUBWAY.

YOU'RE CERTA ANXIO TO G RID ME.

COME IN AT 9:00 –
"HI PHIL –
HI RAY –
HI CHARLIE –"
TALK – READ
THE PAPERS –
IT'S 9:30 –

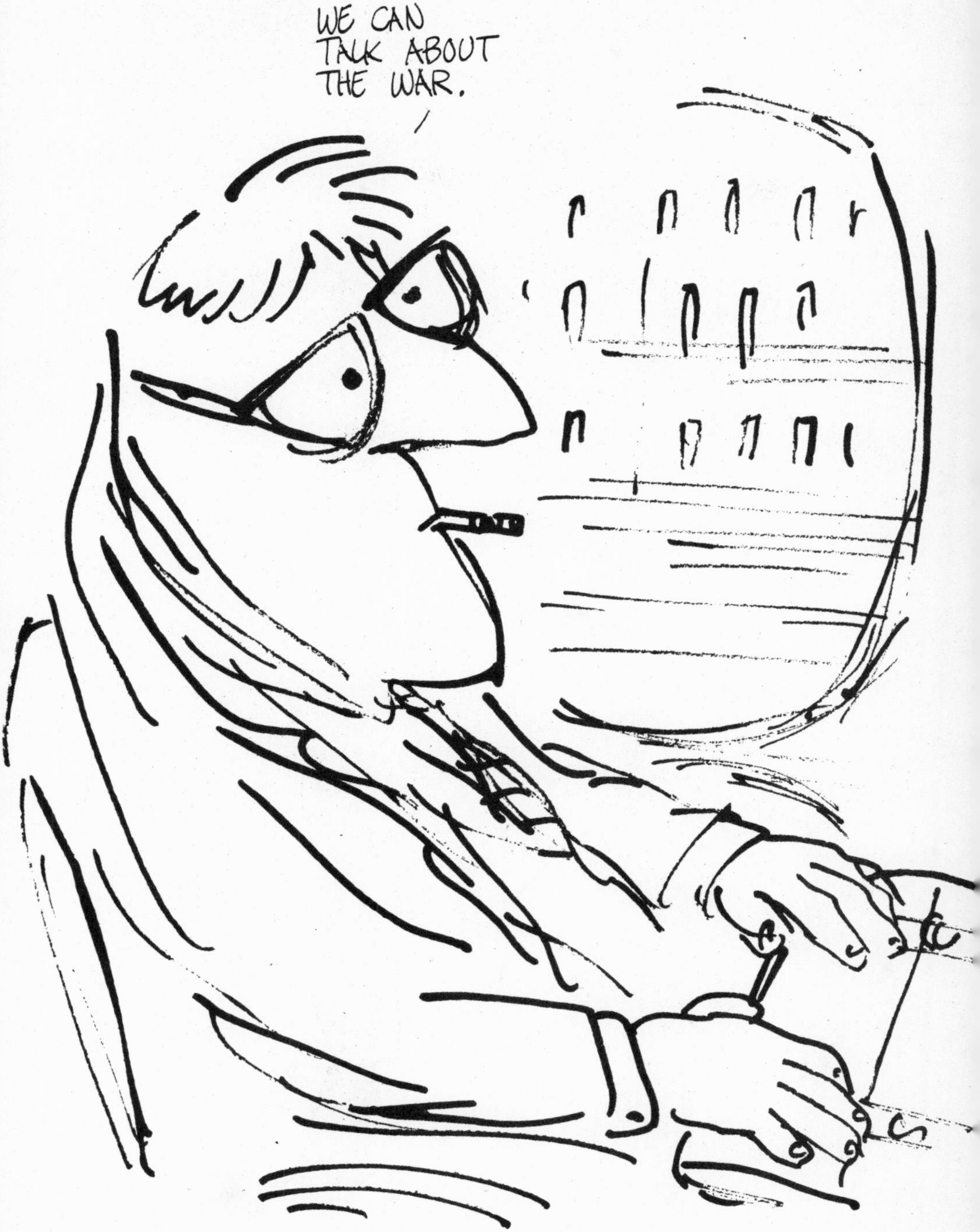
WE CAN TALK ABOUT THE WAR.

DON'T USE MY NAME.

HELLO — AM I
SPEAKING
TO
DOLORES?

WELL MY NAME IS BERNARD
AND I WAS IN THE NEIGHBOR-
HOOD AND A MUTUAL FRIEND
SUGGESTED I CALL YOU.
WHY DON'T I PICK UP
SOME BEER AND DROP
OVER FOR
A WHILE?

7.

8.

SHE
SAID
YES

IT'S AFTER **MIDNIGHT**
AND SHE'S GOING TO
SEE **ME!** **SHE'S**
GOING TO
SEE
ME!

9.

10.

HOW CAN YOU HAVE
ANY RESPECT FOR
SOMEONE LIKE THAT?

11.

THINK IT'LL
SNOW IN TIME
FOR CHRISTMAS?

YEARS AND YEARS AND YEARS AGO WHEN
THERE WERE WOLVES IN WALES - WHEN
WE SANG AND WALLOWED IN CAVES THAT
SMELT LIKE SUNDAY AFTERNOONS IN DAMP
FRONT FARMHOUSE PARLORS, IT
SNOWED AND SNOWED.

THERE WERE PRESENTS THEN -
BAGS OF MOIST AND MANY COLORED
JELLY BABIES, HARDBOILEDS,
TOFFEE, FUDGE AND ALLSORTS
AND TROOPS OF BRIGHT TIN
SOLDIERS WHO IF THEY COULD
NOT FIGHT- COULD ALWAYS RUN -

YEAH,
BUT

NOT MANY THOSE MORNINGS
TROD THE PILING STREETS.
IN THE RICH AND HEAVY
AFTERNOON, THE UNCLES
BREATHING LIKE DOLPHINS
AND THE SNOW DESCEND-
ING, I WOULD SIT AMONG
FESTOONS AND NIBBLE
DATES.

ALL
I
ASKED
WAS—

FOR DINNER WE HAD TURKEY
AND BLAZING PUDDING—AND
AFTER DINNER THERE WAS
MUSIC—A COUSIN SANG
"CHERRY RIPE" AND ANOTHER
SANG "DRAKE'S DRUM."

THE SILENT ONE CLOUDED
HEAVENS DRIFTED ON TO
THE SEA AND THEN I
WENT TO BED.

with apologies to Dylan Thomas

S. S. S.

H

ONE DAY HE COMES HOME - HE SAYS - "MAMMA, I AM NOT WELL EMOTIONALLY. I NEED A PSYCHIATRIST."

SO I SEND HIM TO A PSYCHIATRIST. AFTER ALL IF YOU CAN'T HELP YOUR OWN SON, WHAT'S A MOTHER FOR?

SO ONE DAY HE COMES HOME. HE SAYS - "MAMMA, PSYCHOANALYSIS HAS TAUGHT ME THAT HOME IS A SMOTHERING INFLUENCE. I'M MOVING OUT."

SO I FIND HIM HIS OWN APARTMENT. AFTER ALL IF YOU CAN'T HELP YOUR OWN SON, WHAT'S A MOTHER FOR?

I GIVE HIM RENT MONEY. I GIVE HIM PSYCHIATRIST MONEY. I GIVE HIM A LITTLE EXTRA SO HE COULD ENJOY HIMSELF. LISTEN - WHAT WOULD I DO WITH IT? WHAT'S A MOTHER FOR?

O ONE DAY HE CALLS UP. HE SAYS - MAMMA, YOU ARE GIVING ME ALL THIS MONEY JUST SO I SHOULD FEEL **GUILTY!** GUILT IS A MOTHER'S WEAPON.

ALLRIGHT, WHY ARGUE? WHAT DOES IT GET YOU? SO I STOP PAYING HIS PSYCHIATRIST AND I STOP PAYING HIS RENT AND I STOP GIVING HIM ANYTHING EXTRA.

SO NOW ITS OVER A MONTH - HE'S DISPOSSESSED, HE CAN'T FIND A JOB. HIS PSYCHIATRIST IS SUING HIM.

BUT LISTEN - SO LONG AS HE'S HAPPY.

10

AND THE LAND
SINGS BACK—
"**WHO ARE YOU
KIDDING?
WHO ARE YOU
KIDDING?**"

6.

AND THE FARMER
SINGS—" I'LL
BE **CREATIVE**—
I'LL START ON
THAT **NOVEL**—
CERAMICS AND
JEWELRY— I'LL
HAVE **FULFILL-
MENT**"

7.

AND THE LAND
SINGS BACK—
"CUT OUT THE
NONSENSE.
WHY DON'T YOU
GROW UP.
YOU'LL FEED
ME **FOREVER**."

8.

THEN THERE
IS A WILD
CIRCLE
DANCE
DONE ON
THE KNEES.

9.

IN MY
COUNTRY
IT CAN
GO ON
FOR YEARS.

plink plink

plink

10.

1.

3.

4.

SO I'VE DECIDED TO MARRY SIDNEY.

1.

I TRIED TO BREAK OFF BUT HE'S SO PERSISTENT. HE SAID I WAS HIS LAST CHANCE. IT'S IMPORTANT TO A MARRIAGE TO KNOW YOU'RE DESIRED.

2.

HE'S REALLY FAR MORE SENSITIVE THAN MOST PEOPLE THINK. LIKE I WARNED HIM HOW COMPULSIVE I AM — BUT HE SAID I WAS HIS DARLING GIRL AND HE WOULDN'T LET ME TALK ABOUT MYSELF THAT WAY. OVERLOOKING FAULTS IS VERY IMPORTANT IN A MARRIAGE.

3.

AND HE READS A LOT, TOO. HE MAKES IT HIS BUSINESS TO GET THROUGH "THE NEW YORKER" EVERY WEEK. YOU JUST DON'T NOTICE IT BECAUSE HE NEVER TALKS.

4.

AND I EXPLAINED HOW
VITAL THE DANCE IS
IN MY LIFE AND HE'S
SURE THAT AS SOON AS
HE SEES ONE HE'LL
LOVE IT.
MUTUAL INTERESTS
ARE VERY IMPORTANT
IN A MARRIAGE.

5.

AND, OF COURSE,
ONE CAN'T IGNORE
THAT HE HAS A
FINE FINANCIAL
FUTURE.
HIS FATHER
PROMISED HIM
A RAISE AFTER
THE WEDDING.

6.

AND HE'S
NOT THE TYPE
TO BE
UNREASONABLE
ABOUT PHYSICAL
DEMANDS.

7.

ONCE I GET USED
TO HIM, OURS CAN
BE A VERY RICH
EXPERIENCE.

8.

TAKE A LOOK, CHARLIE —
75 FEET LONG —
500 H.P. — **300**
POUNDS OF CHROME-
PERFUMED EXHAUST —
AND SHE RIDES
LIKE A **DREAM** —
FAN*TAS*TIC*!*

1.

HERE SHE IS, CHARLIE —
16 MM. — SOUND ON FILM —
SELF BLIMPED
AUTO ADJUSTING
ANAMORPHIC ATTACHMENT
WITH A SWITCH BLADE
FOCUS — TAKES PICTURES
LIKE A **DREAM** —
FAN*TAS*TIC*!*

2.

OVER HERE, CHARLIE —
50 INCH — FULL COLOR —
MULTI-IMAGE PICTURE
TUBE WITH A
FLEXI-RESPONSE
CHANNEL SELECTOR —
WORKS LIKE
A **DREAM** —
FAN*TAS*TIC*!*

3.

TAKE A LOOK, CHARLIE —
6 ELECTRO - HYDRO
TWEETERS —
8 WALL TO WALL
WOOFERS — WITH A
1200 WATT PRE-AMP
STEREO OUTPUT — PLAYS
LIKE A **DREAM** —
FAN*TAS*TIC*!*

4.

AND HEAR THIS, CHARLIE —
I RECORD MY OWN
TAPES! JUST LISTEN —
FAN**TAS**TIC!

CLICK

5.

ROAR

6.

THAT WAS AN
H-BOMB BLAST
RECORDED **RIGHT**
ON THE SPOT—
SOUNDS LIKE ITS
IN THE **ROOM**
DOESN'T IT?
FAN**TAS**TIC!

7.

ITS A
FULL
LIFE,
CHARLIE.

8.

A
DANCE
TO
AUTUMN.

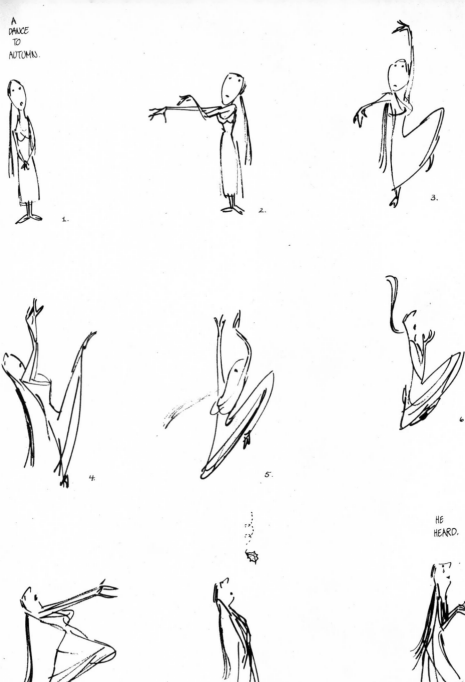

1.

2.

3.

4.

5.

6.

HE
HEARD.

7.

8.

9.